1920

Extract from Captain Stormfield's Visit to Heaven

BY

Mark Twain

NEW YORK AND LONDON
HARPER & BROTHERS

Extract from
Captain Stormfield's
Visit to Heaven

Extract from Captain Stormfield's Visit to Heaven

I

WELL, when I had been dead about thirty years, I begun to get a little anxious. Mind you, I had been whizzing through space all that time, like a comet. *Like* a comet! Why, Peters, I laid over the lot of them! Of course there warn't any of them going my way, as a steady

thing, you know, because they travel
in a long circle like the loop of a lasso,
whereas I was pointed as straight as
a dart for the Hereafter; but I happened on one every now and then
that was going my way for an hour
or so, and then we had a bit of a
brush together. But it was generally
pretty one-sided, because I sailed by
them the same as if they were standing still. An ordinary comet don't
make more than about 200,000 miles
a minute. Of course when I came
across one of that sort—like Encke's
and Halley's comets, for instance—it
warn't anything but just a flash and
a vanish, you see. You couldn't
rightly call it a race. It was as if the
comet was a gravel-train and I was
a telegraph despatch. But after I

got outside of our astronomical system, I used to flush a comet occasionally that was something *like*. *We* haven't got any such comets—ours don't begin. One night I was swinging along at a good round gait, everything taut and trim, and the wind in my favor—I judged I was going about a million miles a minute—it might have been more, it couldn't have been less—when I flushed a most uncommonly big one about three points off my starboard bow. By his stern lights I judged he was bearing about northeast - and - by - north - half - east. Well, it was so near my course that I wouldn't throw away the chance; so I fell off a point, steadied my helm, and went for him. You should have heard me whiz, and seen

3

Extract from Captain

the electric fur fly! In about a
minute and a half I was fringed out
with an electrical nimbus that flamed
around for miles and miles and lit
up all space like broad day. The
comet was burning blue in the distance, like a sickly torch, when I
first sighted him, but he begun to
grow bigger and bigger as I crept up
on him. I slipped up on him so fast
that when I had gone about 150,000,-
000 miles I was close enough to be
swallowed up in the phosphorescent
glory of his wake, and I couldn't see
anything for the glare. Thinks I,
it won't do to run into him, so I
shunted to one side and tore along.
By and by I closed up abreast of his
tail. Do you know what it was like?
It was like a gnat closing up on the

4

continent of America. I forged along.
By and by I had sailed along his coast
for a little upwards of a hundred and
fifty million miles, and then I could
see by the shape of him that I hadn't
even got up to his waistband yet.
Why, Peters, *we* don't know anything
about comets, down here. If you
want to see comets that *are* comets,
you've got to go outside of our solar
system—where there's room for them,
you understand. My friend, I've
seen comets out there that couldn't
even lay down inside the *orbits* of our
noblest comets without their tails
hanging over.

Well, I boomed along another hundred and fifty million miles, and got
up abreast his shoulder, as you may
say. I was feeling pretty fine, I tell

5

you; but just then I noticed the officer of the deck come to the side and hoist his glass in my direction. Straight off I heard him sing out—

"Below there, ahoy! Shake her up, shake her up! Heave on a hundred million billion tons of brimstone!"

"Ay—ay, sir!"

"Pipe the stabboard watch! All hands on deck!"

"Ay—ay, sir!"

"Send two hundred thousand million men aloft to shake out royals and sky-scrapers!"

"Ay—ay, sir!"

"Hand the stuns'ls! Hang out every rag you've got! Clothe her from stem to rudder-post!"

"Ay—ay, sir!"

In about a second I begun to see

Stormfield's Visit to Heaven

I'd woke up a pretty ugly customer, Peters. In less than ten seconds that comet was just a blazing cloud of red-hot canvas. It was piled up into the heavens clean out of sight— the old thing seemed to swell out and occupy all space; the sulphur smoke from the furnaces—oh, well, nobody can describe the way it rolled and tumbled up into the skies, and nobody can half describe the way it smelt. Neither can anybody begin to describe the way that monstrous craft begun to crash along. And such another powwow — thousands of bo's'n's whistles screaming at once, and a crew like the populations of a hundred thousand worlds like ours all swearing at once. Well, I never heard the like of it before.

Extract from Captain

We roared and thundered along
side by side, both doing our level best,
because I'd never struck a comet
before that could lay over me, and
so I was bound to beat this one or
break something. I judged I had
some reputation in space, and I cal-
culated to keep it. I noticed I wasn't
gaining as fast, now, as I was before,
but still I was gaining. There was
a power of excitement on board the
comet. Upwards of a hundred billion
passengers swarmed up from below
and rushed to the side and begun to
bet on the race. Of course this
careened her and damaged her speed.
My, but wasn't the mate mad! He
jumped at that crowd, with his
trumpet in his hand, and sung
out—

8

Stormfield's Visit to Heaven

"Amidships! amidships, you ——!¹ or I'll brain the last idiot of you!"

Well, sir, I gained and gained, little by little, till at last I went skimming sweetly by the magnificent old conflagration's nose. By this time the captain of the comet had been rousted out, and he stood there in the red glare for'ard, by the mate, in his shirt-sleeves and slippers, his hair all rats' nests and one suspender hanging, and how sick those two men did look! I just simply couldn't help putting my thumb to my nose as I glided away and singing out:

"Ta-ta! ta-ta! Any word to send to your family?"

Peters, it was a mistake. Yes, sir,

---

¹ The captain could not remember what this word was. He said it was in a foreign tongue.

9

I've often regretted that—it was a
mistake. You see, the captain had
given up the race, but that remark
was too tedious for him—he couldn't
stand it. He turned to the mate,
and says he—

"Have we got brimstone enough of
our own to make the trip?"

"Yes, sir."

"Sure?"

"Yes, sir—more than enough."

"How much have we got in cargo
for Satan?"

"Eighteen hundred thousand billion quintillions of kazarks."

"Very well, then, let his boarders
freeze till the next comet comes.
Lighten ship! Lively, now, lively,
men! Heave the whole cargo overboard!"

Stormfield's Visit to Heaven

Peters, look me in the eye, and be calm. I found out, over there, that a kazark is exactly the bulk of a *hundred and sixty-nine worlds like ours!* They hove all that load overboard. When it fell it wiped out a considerable raft of stars just as clean as if they'd been candles and somebody blowed them out. As for the race, that was at an end. The minute she was lightened the comet swung along by me the same as if I was anchored. The captain stood on the stern, by the after-davits, and put his thumb to his nose and sung out—

"Ta-ta! ta-ta! Maybe *you've* got some message to send your friends in the Everlasting Tropics!"

Then he hove up his other suspender and started for'ard, and inside of three-quarters of an hour his craft was only a pale torch again in the distance. Yes, it was a mistake, Peters—that remark of mine. I don't reckon I'll ever get over being sorry about it. I'd 'a' beat the bully of the firmament if I'd kept my mouth shut.

But I've wandered a little off the track of my tale; I'll get back on my course again. Now you see what kind of speed I was making. So, as I said, when I had been tearing along this way about thirty years I begun to get uneasy. Oh, it was pleasant enough, with a good deal to find out, but then it was kind of lonesome, you know. Besides, I wanted to get somewhere.

Stormfield's Visit to Heaven

I hadn't shipped with the idea of
cruising forever. First off, I liked
the delay, because I judged I was
going to fetch up in pretty warm
quarters when I got through; but
towards the last I begun to feel that
I'd rather go to — well, most any
place, so as to finish up the uncer-
tainty.

Well, one night—it was always
night, except when I was rushing by
some star that was occupying the
whole universe with its fire and its
glare—light enough then, of course,
but I necessarily left it behind in a
minute or two and plunged into a
solid week of darkness again. The
stars ain't so close together as they
look to be. Where was I? Oh yes;
one night I was sailing along, when I

13

discovered a tremendous long row of
blinking lights away on the horizon
ahead.   As I approached, they begun
to tower and swell and look like
mighty furnaces.   Says I to myself—

"By George, I've arrived at last—
and at the wrong place, just as I
expected!"

Then I fainted.   I don't know how
long I was insensible, but it must have
been a good while, for, when I came to,
the darkness was all gone and there
was the loveliest sunshine and the
balmiest, fragrantest air in its place.
And there was such a marvellous
world spread out before me—such a
glowing, beautiful, bewitching country.   The things I took for furnaces
were gates, miles high, made all of
flashing jewels, and they pierced a

14

wall of solid gold that you couldn't
see the top of, nor yet the end of,
in either direction. I was pointed
straight for one of these gates, and
a-coming like a house afire. Now
I noticed that the skies were black
with millions of people, pointed for
those gates. What a roar they made,
rushing through the air! The ground
was as thick as ants with people,
too—billions of them, I judge.

I lit. I drifted up to a gate with a
swarm of people, and when it was my
turn the head clerk says, in a business-
like way—

"Well, quick! Where are you
from?"

"San Francisco," says I.

"San Fran—*what?*" says he.

"San Francisco."

15

He scratched his head and looked puzzled, then he says—

"Is it a planet?"

By George, Peters, think of it! "*Planet?*" says I; "it's a city. And moreover, it's one of the biggest and finest and—"

"There, there!" says he, "no time here for conversation. We don't deal in cities here. Where are you from in a *general* way?"

"Oh," I says, "I beg your pardon. Put me down for California."

I had him *again*, Peters! He puzzled a second, then he says, sharp and irritable—

"I don't know any such planet—is it a constellation?"

"Oh, my goodness!" says I. "Con-

stellation, says you? No—it's a
State."

"Man, we don't deal in States here.
Will you tell me where you are from
in general—at large, don't you understand?"

"Oh, now I get your idea," I says.
"I'm from America, — the United
States of America."

Peters, do you know I had him
again? If I hadn't I'm a clam! His
face was as blank as a target after a
militia shooting-match. He turned
to an under clerk and says—

"Where is America? *What* is
America?"

The under clerk answered up
prompt and says—

"There ain't any such orb."

"*Orb?*" says I. "Why, what are

you talking about, young man? It ain't an orb; it's a country; it's a continent. Columbus discovered it; I reckon likely you've heard of *him*, anyway. America—why, sir, America—"

"Silence!" says the head clerk. "Once for all, where—are—you—*from?*"

"Well," says I, "I don't know anything more to say—unless I lump things, and just say I'm from the world."

"Ah," says he, brightening up, "now that's something like! *What* world?"

Peters, he had *me*, that time. I looked at him, puzzled, he looked at me, worried. Then he burst out—

"Come, come, what world?"

Says I, "Why, *the* world, of course."

"*The* world!" he says. "H'm! there's billions of them! . . . Next!"

That meant for me to stand aside. I done so, and a sky-blue man with seven heads and only one leg hopped into my place. I took a walk. It just occurred to me, then, that all the myriads I had seen swarming to that gate, up to this time, were just like that creature. I tried to run across somebody I was acquainted with, but they were out of acquaintances of mine just then. So I thought the thing all over and finally sidled back there pretty meek and feeling rather stumped, as you may say.

"Well?" said the head clerk.

"Well, sir," I says, pretty humble, "I don't seem to make out which

world it is I'm from. But you may
know it from this—it's the one the
Saviour saved."

He bent his head at the Name.
Then he says, gently—

"The worlds He has saved are like
to the gates of heaven in number—
none can count them. What astronomical system is your world in?—
perhaps that may assist."

"It's the one that has the sun in
it—and the moon—and Mars"—he
shook his head at each name—hadn't
ever heard of them, you see—"and
Neptune—and Uranus—and Jupiter—"

"Hold on!" says he—"hold on a
minute! Jupiter . . . Jupiter . . .
Seems to me we had a man from there
eight or nine hundred years ago—but

people from that system very seldom
enter by this gate." All of a sudden
he begun to look me so straight in the
eye that I thought he was going to
bore through me. Then he says, very
deliberate, "Did you come *straight
here* from your system?"

"Yes, sir," I says—but I blushed
the least little bit in the world when
I said it.

He looked at me very stern, and
says—

"That is not true; and this is not
the place for prevarication. You
wandered from your course. How
did that happen?"

Says I, blushing again—

"I'm sorry, and I take back what
I said, and confess. I raced a little
with a comet one day—only just

the least little bit—only the tiniest lit—"

"So—so," says he—and without any sugar in his voice to speak of.

I went on, and says—

"But I only fell off just a bare point, and I went right back on my course again the minute the race was over."

"No matter—that divergence has made all this trouble. It has brought you to a gate that is billions of leagues from the right one. If you had gone to your own gate they would have known all about your world at once and there would have been no delay. But we will try to accommodate you." He turned to an under clerk and says—

"What system is Jupiter in?"

Stormfield's Visit to Heaven

"I don't remember, sir, but I think there is such a planet in one of the little new systems away out in one of the thinly worlded corners of the universe. I will see."

He got a balloon and sailed up and up and up, in front of a map that was as big as Rhode Island. He went on up till he was out of sight, and by and by he came down and got something to eat and went up again. To cut a long story short, he kept on doing this for a day or two, and finally he came down and said he thought he had found that solar system, but it might be fly-specks. So he got a microscope and went back. It turned out better than he feared. He had rousted out our system, sure enough. He got me to describe our planet and its distance from the sun, and then he says to his chief—

"Oh, I know the one he means, now, sir. It is on the map. It is called the Wart."

Says I to myself, "Young man, it wouldn't be wholesome for you to go down *there* and call it the Wart."

Well, they let me in, then, and told me I was safe forever and wouldn't have any more trouble.

Then they turned from me and went on with their work, the same as if they considered my case all complete and shipshape. I was a good deal surprised at this, but I was diffident about speaking up and reminding them. I did so hate to do it, you know; it seemed a pity to bother them, they had so much on their hands. Twice I thought I would give up and let the thing go; so twice I started to leave, but immediately I thought what a figure I should cut stepping out amongst the redeemed in such a rig, and that made me hang back and come to anchor again. People got to eying me—clerks, you know—wondering why I didn't get under way. I couldn't stand this long—it was too uncomfortable. So at last I plucked up courage and tipped the head clerk a signal. He says—

"What! you here yet? What's wanting?"

Says I, in a low voice and very confidential, making a trumpet with my hands at his ear—

"I beg pardon, and you mustn't

mind my reminding you, and seeming
to meddle, but hain't you forgot something?"

He studied a second, and says—

"Forgot something? . . . No, not
that I know of."

"Think," says I.

He thought. Then he says—

"No, I can't seem to have forgot
anything. What is it?"

"Look at me," says I, "look me
all over."

He done it.

"Well?" says he.

"Well," says I, "you don't notice anything? If I branched out
amongst the elect looking like this,
wouldn't I attract considerable at-
tention?—wouldn't I be a little conspicuous?"

26

"Well," he says, "I don't see anything the matter. What do you lack?"

"Lack! Why, I lack my harp, and my wreath, and my halo, and my hymn-book, and my palm branch— I lack everything that a body naturally requires up here, my friend."

Puzzled? Peters, he was the worst puzzled man you ever saw. Finally he says—

"Well, you seem to be a curiosity every way a body takes you. I never heard of these things before."

I looked at the man awhile in solid astonishment; then I says—

"Now, I hope you don't take it as an offence, for I don't mean any, but really, for a man that has been in the Kingdom as long as I reckon you have, you do seem to know powerful little about its customs."

"Its customs!" says he. "Heaven is a large place, good friend. Large empires have many and diverse customs. Even small dominions have, as you doubtless know by what you have seen of the matter on a small scale in the Wart. How can you imagine I could ever learn the varied customs of the countless kingdoms of heaven? It makes my head ache to think of it. I know the customs that prevail in those portions inhabited by peoples that are appointed to enter by my own gate—and hark ye, that is quite enough knowledge for one individual to try to pack into his head in the thirty-seven millions of years I have devoted night and day to that

study. But the idea of learning the
customs of the whole appalling ex-
panse of heaven—O man, how in-
sanely you talk! Now I don't doubt
that this odd costume you talk about
is the fashion in that district of heaven
you belong to, but you won't be conspicuous in this section without it."

I felt all right, if that was the case,
so I bade him good-day and left. All
day I walked towards the far end of a
prodigious hall of the office, hoping to
come out into heaven any moment,
but it was a mistake. That hall was
built on the general heavenly plan—
it naturally couldn't be small. At
last I got so tired I couldn't go any
farther; so I sat down to rest, and
begun to tackle the queerest sort of
strangers and ask for information;

but I didn't get any; they couldn't
understand my language, and I could
not understand theirs. I got dread-
fully lonesome. I was so down-
hearted and homesick I wished a
hundred times I never had died. I
turned back, of course. About noon
next day, I got back at last and was
on hand at the booking-office once
more. Says I to the head clerk—

"I begin to see that a man's got to
be in his own heaven to be happy."

"Perfectly correct," says he. "Did
you imagine the same heaven would
suit all sorts of men?"

"Well, I had that idea—but I see
the foolishness of it. Which way am
I to go to get to my district?"

He called the under clerk that had
examined the map, and he gave me

general directions. I thanked him
and started; but he says—

"Wait a minute; it is millions of
leagues from here. Go outside and
stand on that red wishing-carpet:
shut your eyes, hold your breath,
and wish yourself there."

"I'm much obliged," says I; "why
didn't you dart me through when I
first arrived?"

"We have a good deal to think of
here; it was your place to think of it
and ask for it. Good-by; we probably
sha'n't see you in this region for a
thousand centuries or so."

"In that case, *o revoor*," says I.

I hopped onto the carpet and held
my breath and shut my eyes and
wished I was in the booking-office of
my own section. The very next

instant a voice I knew sung out in a business kind of a way—

"A harp and a hymn-book, pair of wings and a halo, size 13, for Cap'n Eli Stormfield, of San Francisco!—make him out a clean bill of health, and let him in."

I opened my eyes. Sure enough, it was a Pi Ute Injun I used to know in Tulare County; mighty good fellow—I remembered being at his funeral, which consisted of him being burnt and the other Injuns gauming their faces with his ashes and howling like wildcats. He was powerful glad to see me, and you may make up your mind I was just as glad to see him, and feel that I was in the right kind of a heaven at last.

Just as far as your eye could reach,

there was swarms of clerks, running
and bustling around, tricking out
thousands of Yanks and Mexicans
and English and A-rabs, and all sorts
of people in their new outfits; and
when they gave me my kit and I
put on my halo and took a look in
the glass, I could have jumped over
a house for joy, I was so happy.
"Now *this* is something like!" says I.
"Now," says I, "I'm all right—show
me a cloud."

Inside of fifteen minutes I was a
mile on my way towards the cloud-
banks and about a million people
along with me. Most of us tried to
fly, but some got crippled and nobody made a success of it. So we
concluded to walk, for the present,
till we had had some wing practice.

Extract from Captain

We begun to meet swarms of folks
who were coming back. Some had
harps and nothing else; some had
hymn-books and nothing else; some
had nothing at all; all of them looked
meek and uncomfortable; one young
fellow hadn't anything left but his
halo, and he was carrying that in his
hand; all of a sudden he offered it to
me and says—

"Will you hold it for me a minute?"
Then he disappeared in the crowd.
I went on. A woman asked me to
hold her palm branch, and then *she*
disappeared. A girl got me to hold
her harp for her, and by George, *she*
disappeared; and so on and so on,
till I was about loaded down to the
guards. Then comes a smiling old
gentleman and asked me to hold *his*

things. I swabbed off the perspiration and says, pretty tart—

"I'll have to get you to excuse me, my friend,—*I* ain't no hat-rack."

About this time I begun to run across piles of those traps, lying in the road. I just quietly dumped my extra cargo along with them. I looked around, and, Peters, that whole nation that was following me were loaded down the same as I'd been. The return crowd had got them to hold their things a minute, you see. They all dumped their loads, too, and we went on.

When I found myself perched on a cloud, with a million other people, I never felt so good in my life. Says I, "Now this is according to the promises; I've been having my doubts, but

35

now I *am* in heaven, sure enough." I gave my palm branch a wave or two, for luck, and then I tautened up my harp - strings and struck in. Well, Peters, you can't imagine anything like the row we made. It was grand to listen to, and made a body thrill all over, but there was considerable many tunes going on at once, and that was a drawback to the harmony, you understand; and then there was a lot of Injun tribes, and they kept up such another war-whooping that they kind of took the tuck out of the music. By and by I quit performing, and judged I'd take a rest. There was quite a nice mild old gentleman sitting next me, and I noticed he didn't take a hand; I encouraged him, but he said he was naturally bashful, and

36

was afraid to try before so many
people. By and by the old gentleman said he never could seem to enjoy music somehow. The fact was,
I was beginning to feel the same way;
but I didn't say anything. Him and
I had a considerable long silence, then,
but of course it warn't noticeable in
that place. After about sixteen or
seventeen hours, during which I
played and sung a little, now and
then—always the same tune, because
I didn't know any other—I laid down
my harp and begun to fan myself with
my palm branch. Then we both got
to sighing pretty regular. Finally,
says he—

"Don't you know any tune but the
one you've been pegging at all day?"

"Not another blessed one," says I.

"Don't you reckon you could learn another one?" says he.

"Never," says I; "I've tried to, but I couldn't manage it."

"It's a long time to hang to the one—eternity, you know."

"Don't break my heart," says I; "I'm getting low-spirited enough already."

After another long silence, says he—

"Are you glad to be here?"

Says I, "Old man, I'll be frank with you. This *ain't* just as near my idea of bliss as I thought it was going to be, when I used to go to church."

Says he, "What do you say to knocking off and calling it half a day?"

"That's me," says I. "I never

wanted to get off watch so bad in my life."

So we started. Millions were coming to the cloud-bank all the time, happy and hosannahing; millions were leaving it all the time, looking mighty quiet, I tell you. We laid for the new-comers, and pretty soon I'd got them to hold all my things a minute, and then I was a free man again and most outrageously happy. Just then I ran across old Sam Bartlett, who had been dead a long time, and stopped to have a talk with him. Says I—

"Now tell me—is this to go on forever? Ain't there anything else for a change?"

Says he—

"I'll set you right on that point

very quick. People take the figurative language of the Bible and the allegories for literal, and the first thing they ask for when they get here is a halo and a harp, and so on. Nothing that's harmless and reasonable is refused a body here, if he asks it in the right spirit. So they are outfitted with these things without a word. They go and sing and play just about one day, and that's the last you'll ever see them in the choir. They don't need anybody to tell them that that sort of thing wouldn't make a heaven—at least not a heaven that a sane man could stand a week and remain sane. That cloud - bank is placed where the noise can't disturb the old inhabitants, and so there ain't any harm in letting everybody get up there and cure himself as soon as he comes.

"Now you just remember this— heaven is as blissful and lovely as it can be; but it's just the busiest place you ever heard of. There ain't any idle people here after the first day. Singing hymns and waving palm branches through all eternity is pretty when you hear about it in the pulpit, but it's as poor a way to put in valuable time as a body could contrive. It would just make a heaven of warbling ignoramuses, don't you see? Eternal Rest sounds comforting in the pulpit, too. Well, you try it once, and see how heavy time will hang on your hands. Why, Stormfield, a man like you, that had been active and stirring all his life, would go mad

41

in six months in a heaven where he hadn't anything to do. Heaven is the very last place to come to *rest* in,— and don't you be afraid to bet on that!"

Says I—

"Sam, I'm as glad to hear it as I thought I'd be sorry. I'm glad I come, now."

Says he—

"Cap'n, ain't you pretty physically tired?"

Says I—

"Sam, it ain't any name for it! I'm dog-tired."

"Just so—just so. You've earned a good sleep, and you'll get it. You've earned a good appetite, and you'll enjoy your dinner. It's the same here as it is on earth—you've

got to earn a thing, square and honest,
before you enjoy it. You can't enjoy first and earn afterwards. But
there's this difference, here: you can
choose your own occupation, and all
the powers of heaven will be put
forth to help you make a success of it,
if you do your level best. The shoemaker on earth that had the soul of
a poet in him won't have to make
shoes here."

"Now that's all reasonable and
right," says I. "Plenty of work, and
the kind you hanker after; no more
pain, no more suffering—"

"Oh, hold on; there's plenty of
pain here—but it don't kill. There's
plenty of suffering here, but it don't
last. You see, happiness ain't a
thing in itself — it's only a *contrast*

43

with something that ain't pleasant.
That's all it is. There ain't a thing
you can mention that is happiness in
its own self—it's only so by contrast
with the other thing. And so, as
soon as the novelty is over and the
force of the contrast dulled, it ain't
happiness any longer, and you have
to get something fresh. Well, there's
plenty of pain and suffering in heaven
—consequently there's plenty of con-
trasts, and just no end of happiness."

Says I, "It's the sensiblest heaven
I've heard of yet, Sam, though it's
about as different from the one I was
brought up on as a live princess is
different from her own wax figger."

Along in the first months I knocked
around about the Kingdom, making

friends and looking at the country, and finally settled down in a pretty likely region, to have a rest before taking another start. I went on making acquaintances and gathering up information. I had a good deal of talk with an old bald-headed angel by the name of Sandy McWilliams. He was from somewhere in New Jersey. I went about with him, considerable. We used to lay around, warm afternoons, in the shade of a rock, on some meadow-ground that was pretty high and out of the marshy slush of his cranberry-farm, and there we used to talk about all kinds of things, and smoke pipes. One day, says I—

"About how old might you be, Sandy?"

Extract from Captain

"Seventy-two."

"I judged so.   How long you been in heaven?"

"Twenty-seven years, come Christmas."

"How old was you when you come up?"

"Why, seventy-two, of course."

"You can't mean it!"

"Why can't I mean it?"

"Because, if you was seventy-two then, you are naturally ninety-nine now."

"No, but I ain't.   I stay the same age I was when I come."

"Well," says I, "come to think, there's something just here that I want to ask about.   Down below, I always had an idea that in heaven we would all be young, and bright, and spry."

46

Stormfield's Visit to Heaven

"Well, you *can* be young if you want to. You've only got to wish."

"Well, then, why didn't you wish?"

"I did. They all do. You'll try it, some day, like enough; but you'll get tired of the change pretty soon."

"Why?"

"Well, I'll tell you. Now you've always been a sailor; did you ever try some other business?"

"Yes, I tried keeping grocery, once, up in the mines; but I couldn't stand it; it was too dull—no stir, no storm, no life about it; it was like being part dead and part alive, both at the same time. I wanted to be one thing or t'other. I shut up shop pretty quick and went to sea."

"That's it. Grocery people like it, but you couldn't. You see you

47

wasn't used to it. Well, I wasn't
used to being young, and I couldn't
seem to take any interest in it. I
was strong, and handsome, and had
curly hair, — yes, and wings, too! —
gay wings like a butterfly. I went to
picnics and dances and parties with
the fellows, and tried to carry on and
talk nonsense with the girls, but it
wasn't any use; I couldn't take to it—
fact is, it was an awful bore. What I
wanted was early to bed and early to
rise, and something to *do;* and when
my work was done, I wanted to sit
quiet, and smoke and think—not tear
around with a parcel of giddy young
kids. You can't think what I suf-
fered whilst I was young."

"How long was you young?"

"Only two weeks. That was plenty

48

for me. Laws, I was so lonesome!
You see, I was full of the knowledge
and experience of seventy-two years;
the deepest subject those young folks
could strike was only *a-b-c* to me.
And to hear them argue—oh, my!
it would have been funny, if it hadn't
been so pitiful. Well, I was so
hungry for the ways and the sober
talk I was used to, that I tried to ring
in with the old people, but they
wouldn't have it. They considered
me a conceited young upstart, and
gave me the cold shoulder. Two
weeks was a-plenty for me. I was
glad to get back my bald head again,
and my pipe, and my old drowsy re-
flections in the shade of a rock or a
tree."

"Well," says I, "do you mean to

49

say you're going to stand still at seventy-two, forever?"

"I don't know, and I ain't particular. But I ain't going to drop back to twenty-five any more—I know that, mighty well. I know a sight more than I did twenty-seven years ago, and I enjoy learning, all the time, but I don't seem to get any older. That is, bodily—my mind gets older, and stronger, and better seasoned, and more satisfactory."

Says I, "If a man comes here at ninety, don't he ever set himself back?"

"Of course he does. He sets himself back to fourteen; tries it a couple of hours, and feels like a fool; sets himself forward to twenty; it ain't much improvement; tries thirty, fifty, eighty, and finally ninety—finds he is more at home and comfortable at the same old figure he is used to than any other way. Or, if his mind begun to fail him on earth at eighty, that's where he finally sticks up here. He sticks at the place where his mind was last at its best, for there's where his enjoyment is best, and his ways most set and established."

"Does a chap of twenty-five stay always twenty-five, and look it?"

"If he is a fool, yes. But if he is bright, and ambitious and industrious, the knowledge he gains and the experiences he has, change his ways and thoughts and likings, and make him find his best pleasure in the company of people above that age; so he allows his body to take on that look of as

many added years as he needs to
make him comfortable and proper in
that sort of society; he lets his body
go on taking the look of age, according as he progresses, and by and by
he will be bald and wrinkled outside,
and wise and deep within."

"Babies the same?"

"Babies the same. Laws, what
asses we used to be, on earth, about
these things! We said we'd be always young in heaven. We didn't
say *how* young—we didn't think of
that, perhaps—that is, we didn't all
think alike, anyway. When I was a
boy of seven, I suppose I thought
we'd all be twelve, in heaven; when I
was twelve, I suppose I thought we'd
all be eighteen or twenty in heaven;
when I was forty, I begun to go back;

Stormfield's Visit to Heaven

I remember I hoped we'd all be about *thirty* years old in heaven. Neither a man nor a boy ever thinks the age he *has* is exactly the best one—he puts the *right* age a few years older or a few years younger than he is. Then he makes that ideal age the general age of the heavenly people. And he expects everybody *to stick* at that age—stand stock-still—and expects them to enjoy it!—Now just think of the idea of standing still in heaven! Think of a heaven made up entirely of hoop-rolling, marble-playing cubs of seven years!—or of awkward, diffident, sentimental immaturities of nineteen!—or of vigorous people of thirty, healthy-minded, brimming with ambition, but chained hand and foot to that one age and its limitations like so many helpless galley-slaves! Think of the dull sameness of a society made up of people all of one age and one set of looks, habits, tastes and feelings. Think how superior to it earth would be, with its variety of types and faces and ages, and the enlivening attrition of the myriad interests that come into pleasant collision in such a variegated society."

"Look here," says I, "do you know what you're doing?"

"Well, what am I doing?"

"You are making heaven pretty comfortable in one way, but you are playing the mischief with it in another."

"How d'you mean?"

"Well," I says, "take a young mother that's lost her child, and—"

Stormfield's Visit to Heaven

"'Sh!" he says. "Look!"

It was a woman. Middle-aged, and had grizzled hair. She was walking slow, and her head was bent down, and her wings hanging limp and droopy; and she looked ever so tired, and was crying, poor thing! She passed along by, with her head down, that way, and the tears running down her face, and didn't see us. Then Sandy said, low and gentle, and full of pity:

"*She's* hunting for her child! No, *found* it, I reckon. Lord, how she's changed! But I recognized her in a minute, though it's twenty-seven years since I saw her. A young mother she was, about twenty two or four, or along there; and blooming and lovely and sweet? oh, just a

55

flower! And all her heart and all her
soul was wrapped up in her child, her
little girl, two years old. And it
died, and she went wild with grief,
just wild! Well, the only comfort
she had was that she'd see her child
again, in heaven—'never more to
part,' she said, and kept on saying it
over and over, 'never more to part.'
And the words made her happy; yes,
they did; they made her joyful;
and when I was dying, twenty-seven
years ago, she told me to find her
child the first thing, and say she was
coming—'soon, soon, *very* soon, she
hoped and believed!'"

"Why, it's pitiful, Sandy."

He didn't say anything for a while,
but sat looking at the ground, thinking. Then he says, kind of mournful:

"And now she's come!"

"Well? Go on."

"Stormfield, maybe she hasn't found the child, but *I* think she has. Looks so to me. I've seen cases before. You see, she's kept that child in her head just the same as it was when she jounced it in her arms a little chubby thing. But here it didn't elect to *stay* a child. No, it elected to grow up, which it did. And in these twenty-seven years it has learned all the deep scientific learning there is to learn, and is studying and studying and learning and learning more and more, all the time, and don't give a damn for anything *but* learning; just learning, and discussing gigantic problems with people like herself."

"Well?"

"Stormfield, don't you see? Her
mother knows *cranberries*, and how
to tend them, and pick them, and
put them up, and market them; and
not another blamed thing! Her and
her daughter can't be any more company for each other *now* than mud
turtle and bird o' paradise. Poor
thing, she was looking for a baby to
jounce; *I* think she's struck a dis-
app'intment."

"Sandy, what will they do—stay
unhappy forever in heaven?"

"No, they'll come together and get
adjusted by and by. But not this
year, and not next. By and by."

II

I HAD been having considerable trouble with my wings. The day after I helped the choir I made a dash or two with them, but was not lucky. First off, I flew thirty yards, and then fouled an Irishman and brought him down— brought us both down, in fact. Next, I had a collision with a Bishop—and bowled him down, of course. We had some sharp words, and I felt pretty cheap, to come banging into a grave old person like that, with a

million strangers looking on and
smiling to themselves.

I saw I hadn't got the hang of the
steering, and so couldn't rightly tell
where I was going to bring up when I
started. I went afoot the rest of the
day, and let my wings hang. Early
next morning I went to a private place
to have some practice. I got up on a
pretty high rock, and got a good start,
and went swooping down, aiming for
a bush a little over three hundred
yards off; but I couldn't seem to cal-
culate for the wind, which was about
two points abaft my beam. I could
see I was going considerable to looard
of the bush, so I worked my starboard
wing slow and went ahead strong on
the port one, but it wouldn't answer;
I could see I was going to broach to,

so I slowed down on both, and lit.
I went back to the rock and took
another chance at it. I aimed two
or three points to starboard of the
bush—yes, more than that—enough
so as to make it nearly a head-wind.
I done well enough, but made pretty
poor time. I could see, plain enough,
that on a head-wind, wings was a
mistake. I could see that a body
could sail pretty close to the wind,
but he couldn't go in the wind's eye.
I could see that if I wanted to go
a-visiting any distance from home, and
the wind was ahead, I might have to
wait days, maybe, for a change; and
I could see, too, that these things
could not be any use at all in a gale; if
you tried to run before the wind, you
would make a mess of it, for there

isn't any way to shorten sail—like reefing, you know—you have to take it *all* in—shut your feathers down flat to your sides. That would *land* you, of course. You could lay to, with your head to the wind—that is the best you could do, and right hard work you'd find it, too. If you tried any other game, you would founder, sure.

I judge it was about a couple of weeks or so after this that I dropped old Sandy McWilliams a note one day —it was a Tuesday—and asked him to come over and take his manna and quails with me next day; and the first thing he did when he stepped in was to twinkle his eye in a sly way, and say,—

"Well, Cap, what you done with your wings?"

I saw in a minute that there was some sarcasm done up in that rag somewheres, but I never let on. I only says,—

"Gone to the wash."

"Yes," he says, in a dry sort of way, "they mostly go to the wash—about this time—I've often noticed it. Fresh angels are powerful neat. When do you look for 'em back?"

"Day after to-morrow," says I.

He winked at me, and smiled.

Says I,—

"Sandy, out with it. Come—no secrets among friends. I notice you don't ever wear wings—and plenty others don't. I've been making an ass of myself—is that it?"

"That is about the size of it. But it is no harm. We all do it at first.

63

Extract from Captain

It's perfectly natural. You see, on earth we jump to such foolish conclusions as to things up here. In the pictures we always saw the angels with wings on—and that was all right; but we jumped to the conclusion that that was their way of getting around —and that was all wrong. The wings ain't anything but a uniform, that's all. When they are in the field—so to speak,—they always wear them; you never see an angel going with a message anywhere without his wings, any more than you would see a military officer presiding at a court-martial without his uniform, or a postman delivering letters, or a policeman walking his beat, in plain clothes. But they ain't to *fly* with! The wings are for show, not for use. Old

experienced angels are like officers
of the regular army — they dress
plain, when they are off duty. New
angels are like the militia—never shed
the uniform — always fluttering and
floundering around in their wings,
butting people down, flapping here,
and there, and everywhere, always
imagining they are attracting the
admiring eye—well, they just think
they are the very most important
people in heaven. And when you see
one of them come sailing around with
one wing tipped up and t'other down,
you make up your mind he is saying
to himself: 'I wish Mary Ann in
Arkansaw could see me now. I
reckon she'd wish she hadn't shook
me.' No, they're just for show, that's
all—only just for show."

Extract from Captain

"I judge you've got it about right, Sandy," says I.

"Why, look at it yourself," says he. "*You* ain't built for wings—no man is. You know what a grist of years it took you to come here from the earth—and yet you were booming along faster than any cannon-ball could go. Suppose you had to fly that distance with your wings—wouldn't eternity have been over before you got here? Certainly. Well, angels have to go to the earth every day—millions of them—to appear in visions to dying children and good people, you know—it's the heft of their business. They appear with their wings, of course, because they are on official service, and because the dying persons wouldn't know they

66

were angels if they hadn't wings—but do you reckon they fly with them? It stands to reason they don't. The wings would wear out before they got half-way; even the pin-feathers would be gone; the wing frames would be as bare as kite sticks before the paper is pasted on. The distances in heaven are billions of times greater; angels have to go all over heaven every day; could they do it with their wings alone? No, indeed; they wear the wings for style, but they travel any distance in an instant by *wishing*. The wishing-carpet of the Arabian Nights was a sensible idea—but our earthly idea of angels flying these awful distances with their clumsy wings was foolish.

"Our young saints, of both sexes,

wear wings all the time—blazing red ones, and blue and green, and gold, and variegated, and rainbowed, and ring-streaked-and-striped ones — and nobody finds fault. It is suitable to their time of life. The things are beautiful, and they set the young people off. They are the most striking and lovely part of their outfit—a halo don't *begin*."

"Well," says I, "I've tucked mine away in the cupboard, and I allow to let them lay there till there's mud."

"Yes—or a reception."

"What's that?"

"Well, you can see one to-night if you want to. There's a barkeeper from Jersey City going to be received."

"Go on—tell me about it."

Stormfield's Visit to Heaven

"This barkeeper got converted at a Moody and Sankey meeting, in New York, and started home on the ferryboat, and there was a collision and he got drowned. He is of a class that think all heaven goes wild with joy when a particularly hard lot like him is saved; they think all heaven turns out hosannahing to welcome them; they think there isn't anything talked about in the realms of the blest but their case, for that day. This barkeeper thinks there hasn't been such another stir here in years, as his coming is going to raise.—And I've always noticed this peculiarity about a dead barkeeper — he not only expects all hands to turn out when he arrives, but he expects to be received with a torchlight procession."

Extract from Captain

"I reckon he is disappointed, then."

"No, he isn't. No man is allowed to be disappointed here. Whatever he wants, when he comes—that is, any reasonable and unsacrilegious thing—he can have. There's always a few millions or billions of young folks around who don't want any better entertainment than to fill up their lungs and swarm out with their torches and have a high time over a barkeeper. It tickles the barkeeper till he can't rest, it makes a charming lark for the young folks, it don't do anybody any harm, it don't cost a rap, and it keeps up the place's reputation for making all comers happy and content."

"Very good. I'll be on hand and see them land the barkeeper."

Stormfield's Visit to Heaven

"It is manners to go in full dress. You want to wear your wings, you know, and your other things."

"Which ones?"

"Halo, and harp, and palm branch, and all that."

"Well," says I, "I reckon I ought to be ashamed of myself, but the fact is I left them laying around that day I resigned from the choir. I haven't got a rag to wear but this robe and the wings."

"That's all right. You'll find they've been raked up and saved for you. Send for them."

"I'll do it, Sandy. But what was it you was saying about unsacrilegious things, which people expect to get, and will be disappointed about?"

"Oh, there are a lot of such things

that people expect and don't get.
For instance, there's a Brooklyn
preacher by the name of Talmage,
who is laying up a considerable dis-
appointment for himself. He says,
every now and then in his sermons,
that the first thing he does when he
gets to heaven, will be to fling his
arms around Abraham, Isaac and
Jacob, and kiss them and weep on
them. There's millions of people
down there on earth that are promis-
ing themselves the same thing. As
many as sixty thousand people arrive
here every single day, that want to
run straight to Abraham, Isaac and
Jacob, and hug them and weep on
them. Now mind you, sixty thousand a day is a pretty heavy contract
for those old people. If they were a

mind to allow it, they wouldn't ever
have anything to do, year in and year
out, but stand up and be hugged and
wept on thirty-two hours in the twen-
ty-four. They would be tired out and
as wet as muskrats all the time. What
would heaven be, to *them?* It would
be a mighty good place to get out of—
you know that, yourself. Those are
kind and gentle old Jews, but they
ain't any fonder of kissing the emo-
tional highlights of Brooklyn than you
be. You mark my words, Mr. T.'s
endearments are going to be declined,
with thanks. There are limits to the
privileges of the elect, even in heaven.
Why, if Adam was to show himself
to every new comer that wants to call
and gaze at him and strike him for
his autograph, he would never have

time to do anything else but just that.
Talmage has said he is going to give
Adam some of his attentions, as
well as A., I. and J. But he will
have to change his mind about
that."

· "Do you think Talmage will really
come here?"

"Why, certainly, he will; but don't
you be alarmed; he will run with his
own kind, and there's plenty of them.
That is the main charm of heaven—
there's all kinds here—which wouldn't
be the case if you let the preachers
tell it. Anybody can find the sort
he prefers, here, and he just lets the
others alone, and they let him alone.
When the Deity builds a heaven, it
is built right, and on a liberal
plan."

Sandy sent home for his things, and
I sent for mine, and about nine in the
evening we begun to dress. Sandy
says,—

"This is going to be a grand time
for you, Stormy. Like as not some
of the patriarchs will turn out."

"No, but will they?"

"Like as not. Of course they are
pretty exclusive. They hardly ever
show themselves to the common public. I believe they never turn out
except for an eleventh-hour convert.
They wouldn't do it then, only
earthly tradition makes a grand show
pretty necessary on that kind of an
occasion."

"Do they all turn out, Sandy?"

"Who?—all the patriarchs? Oh,
no—hardly ever more than a couple.

You will be here fifty thousand years
—maybe more—before you get a
glimpse of all the patriarchs and
prophets. Since I have been here,
Job has been to the front once, and
once Ham and Jeremiah both at the
same time. But the finest thing that
has happened in my day was a year
or so ago; that was Charles Peace's
reception—him they called 'the Ban-
nercross Murderer'—an Englishman.
There were four patriarchs and two
prophets on the Grand Stand that
time — there hasn't been anything
like it since Captain Kidd came; Abel
was there — the first time in twelve
hundred years. A report got around
that Adam was coming; well, of
course, Abel was enough to bring a
crowd, all by himself, but there is no-

body that can draw like Adam. It
was a false report, but it got around,
anyway, as I say, and it will be a long
day before I see the like of it again.
The reception was in the English
department, of course, which is eight
hundred and eleven million miles from
the New Jersey line. I went, along
with a good many of my neighbors,
and it was a sight to see, I can tell you.
Flocks came from all the depart-
ments. I saw Esquimaux there, and
Tartars, negroes, Chinamen—people
from everywhere. You see a mixture
like that in the Grand Choir, the first
day you land here, but you hardly
ever see it again. There were billions
of people; when they were singing or
hosannahing, the noise was wonderful; and even when their tongues were

still the drumming of the wings was nearly enough to burst your head, for all the sky was as thick as if it was snowing angels. Although Adam was not there, it was a great time anyway, because we had three archangels on the Grand Stand—it is a seldom thing that even one comes out."

"What did they look like, Sandy?"

"Well, they had shining faces, and shining robes, and wonderful rainbow wings, and they stood eighteen feet high, and wore swords, and held their heads up in a noble way, and looked like soldiers."

"Did they have halos?"

"No—anyway, not the hoop kind. The archangels and the upper-class patriarchs wear a finer thing than that. It is a round, solid, splendid

glory of gold, that is blinding to look
at. You have often seen a patriarch
in a picture, on earth, with that thing
on—you remember it?—he looks as
if he had his head in a brass platter.
That don't give you the right idea of
it at all—it is much more shining and
beautiful."

"Did you talk with those archangels and patriarchs, Sandy?"

"Who—*I?* Why, what can you
be thinking about, Stormy? I ain't
worthy to speak to such as they."

"Is Talmage?"

"Of course not. You have got
the same mixed-up idea about these
things that everybody has down
there. I had it once, but I got over
it. Down there they talk of the
heavenly King—and that is right—

79

but then they go right on speaking as
if this was a republic and everybody
was on a dead level with everybody
else, and privileged to fling his arms
around anybody he comes across, and
be hail-fellow-well-met with all the
elect, from the highest down. How
tangled up and absurd that is! How
are you going to have a republic under
a king? How are you going to have
a republic at all, where the head of
the government is absolute, holds his
place forever, and has no parliament,
no council to meddle or make in his
affairs, nobody voted for, nobody
elected, nobody in the whole universe
with a voice in the government, nobody asked to take a hand in its
matters, and nobody *allowed* to do
it? Fine republic, ain't it?"

Stormfield's Visit to Heaven

"Well, yes—it *is* a little different from the idea I had—but I thought I might go around and get acquainted with the grandees, anyway—not exactly splice the main-brace with them, you know, but shake hands and pass the time of day."

"Could Tom, Dick and Harry call on the Cabinet of Russia and do that? — on Prince Gortschakoff, for instance?"

"I reckon not, Sandy."

"Well, this is Russia—only more so. There's not the shadow of a republic about it anywhere. There are ranks, here. There are viceroys, princes, governors, sub-governors, sub-sub-governors, and a hundred orders of nobility, grading along down from grand-ducal archangels, stage by stage, till the general level is struck, where there ain't any titles. Do you know what a prince of the blood is, on earth?"

"No."

"Well, a prince of the blood don't belong to the royal family exactly, and he don't belong to the mere nobility of the kingdom; he is lower than the one, and higher than t'other. That's about the position of the patriarchs and prophets here. There's some mighty high nobility here— people that you and I ain't worthy to polish sandals for—and *they* ain't worthy to polish sandals for the patriarchs and prophets. That gives you a kind of an idea of their rank, don't it? You begin to see how high up they are, don't you? Just to get

a two-minute glimpse of one of them
is a thing for a body to remember
and tell about for a thousand years.
Why, Captain, just think of this:
if Abraham was to set his foot down
here by this door, there would be a
railing set up around that foot-track
right away, and a shelter put over it,
and people would flock here from all
over heaven, for hundreds and hundreds of years, to look at it. Abraham
is one of the parties that Mr. Talmage,
of Brooklyn, is going to embrace, and
kiss, and weep on, when he comes.
He wants to lay in a good stock of
tears, you know, or five to one he will
go dry before he gets a chance to do
it."

"Sandy," says I, "I had an idea
that I was going to be equals with

83

everybody here, too, but I will let
that drop. It don't matter, and I
am plenty happy enough anyway."

"Captain, you are happier than
you would be, the other way. These
old patriarchs and prophets have got
ages the start of you; they know more
in two minutes than you know in a
year. Did you ever try to have a
sociable improving-time discussing
winds, and currents and variations of
compass with an undertaker?"

"I get your idea, Sandy. He
couldn't interest me. He would be
an ignoramus in such things—he
would bore me, and I would bore
him."

"You have got it. You would bore
the patriarchs when you talked, and
when they talked they would shoot

84

over your head. By and by you
would say, 'Good morning, your
Eminence, I will call again' — but
you wouldn't. Did you ever ask the
slush-boy to come up in the cabin
and take dinner with you?"

"I get your drift again, Sandy. I
wouldn't be used to such grand people
as the patriarchs and prophets, and I
would be sheepish and tongue-tied in
their company, and mighty glad to
get out of it. Sandy, which is the
highest rank, patriarch or prophet?"

"Oh, the prophets hold over the
patriarchs. The newest prophet,
even, is of a sight more consequence
than the oldest patriarch. Yes, sir,
Adam himself has to walk behind
Shakespeare."

"Was Shakespeare a prophet?"

Extract from Captain

"Of course he was; and so was Homer, and heaps more. But Shakespeare and the rest have to walk behind a common tailor from Tennessee, by the name of Billings; and behind a horse-doctor named Sakka, from Afghanistan. Jeremiah, and Billings and Buddha walk together, side by side, right behind a crowd from planets not in our astronomy; next come a dozen or two from Jupiter and other worlds; next come Daniel, and Sakka and Confucius; next a lot from systems outside of ours; next come Ezekiel, and Mahomet, Zoroaster, and a knife-grinder from ancient Egypt; then there is a long string, and after them, away down toward the bottom, come Shakespeare and Homer, and a shoemaker named Marais, from the back settlements of France."

"Have they really rung in Mahomet and all those other heathens?"

"Yes—they all had their message, and they all get their reward. The man who don't get his reward on earth, needn't bother—he will get it here, sure."

"But why did they throw off on Shakespeare, that way, and put him away down there below those shoe-makers and horse-doctors and knife-grinders—a lot of people nobody ever heard of?"

"That is the heavenly justice of it —they warn't rewarded according to their deserts, on earth, but here they get their rightful rank. That tailor Billings, from Tennessee, wrote poetry that Homer and Shakespeare couldn't begin to come up to; but nobody would print it, nobody read it but his neighbors, an ignorant lot, and they laughed at it. Whenever the village had a drunken frolic and a dance, they would drag him in and crown him with cabbage leaves, and pretend to bow down to him; and one night when he was sick and nearly starved to death, they had him out and crowned him, and then they rode him on a rail about the village, and everybody followed along, beating tin pans and yelling. Well, he died before morning. He wasn't ever expecting to go to heaven, much less that there was going to be any fuss made over him, so I reckon he was a good deal surprised when the reception broke on him."

"Was you there, Sandy?"

"Bless you, no!"

"Why? Didn't you know it was going to come off?"

"Well, I judge I did. It was the talk of these realms—not for a day, like this barkeeper business, but for twenty years before the man died."

"Why the mischief didn't you go, then?"

"Now how you talk! The like of me go meddling around at the reception of a prophet? A mudsill like me trying to push in and help receive an awful grandee like Edward J. Billings? Why, I should have been laughed at for a billion miles around. I shouldn't ever heard the last of it."

"Well, who did go, then?"

"Mighty few people that you and I

will ever get a chance to see, Captain.
Not a solitary commoner ever has the
luck to see a reception of a prophet,
I can tell you. All the nobility,
and all the patriarchs and prophets—
every last one of them—and all the
archangels, and all the princes and
governors and viceroys, were there,—
and *no* small fry—not a single one.
And mind you, I'm not talking about
only the grandees from *our* world,
but the princes and patriarchs and
so on from *all* the worlds that shine
in our sky, and from billions more
that belong in systems upon systems
away outside of the one our sun is in.
There were some prophets and patriarchs there that ours ain't a circum-
stance to, for rank and illustrious-
ness and all that. Some were from

Jupiter and other worlds in our own
system, but the most celebrated were
three poets, Saa, Bo and Soof, from
great planets in three different and
very remote systems. These three
names are common and familiar in
every nook and corner of heaven,
clear from one end of it to the other—
fully as well known as the eighty
Supreme Archangels, in fact—whereas our Moses, and Adam, and the rest,
have not been heard of outside of our
world's little corner of heaven, except
by a few very learned men scattered
here and there—and they always spell
their names wrong, and get the per-
formances of one mixed up with the
doings of another, and they almost
always locate them simply *in our solar
system*, and think that is enough with-

out going into little details such as naming the particular world they are from. It is like a learned Hindoo showing off how much he knows by saying Longfellow lives in the United States—as if he lived all over the United States, and as if the country was so small you couldn't throw a brick there without hitting him. Between you and me, it does gravel me, the cool way people from those monster worlds outside our system snub our little world, and even our system. Of course we think a good deal of Jupiter, because our world is only a potato to it, for size; but then there are worlds in other systems that Jupiter isn't even a mustard-seed to — like the planet Goobra, for instance, which you

couldn't squeeze inside the orbit of
Halley's comet without straining the
rivets. Tourists from Goobra (I mean
parties that lived and died there—
natives) come here, now and then,
and inquire about our world, and
when they find out it is so little that
a streak of lightning can flash clear
around it in the eighth of a second,
they have to lean up against something to laugh. Then they screw a
glass into their eye and go to examin-
ing *us*, as if we were a curious kind of
foreign bug, or something of that sort.
One of them asked me how long our
day was; and when I told him it was
twelve hours long, as a general thing,
he asked me if people where I was
from considered it worth while to get
up and wash for such a day as that.

93

That is the way with those Goobra
people—they can't seem to let a
chance go by to throw it in your face
that their day is three hundred and
twenty-two of our years long. This
young snob was just of age—he was
six or seven thousand of his days old
—say two million of our years—and
he had all the puppy airs that belong
to that time of life — that turning-
point when a person has got over being a boy and yet ain't quite a man
exactly. If it had been anywhere else
but in heaven, I would have given him
a piece of my mind. Well, anyway,
Billings had the grandest reception
that has been seen in thousands of
centuries, and I think it will have a
good effect. His name will be carried
pretty far, and it will make our system

talked about, and maybe our world, too, and raise us in the respect of the general public of heaven. Why, look here—Shakespeare walked backwards before that tailor from Tennessee, and scattered flowers for him to walk on, and Homer stood behind his chair and waited on him at the banquet. Of course that didn't go for much *there*, amongst all those big foreigners from other systems, as they hadn't heard of Shakespeare or Homer either, but it would amount to considerable down there on our little earth if they could know about it. I wish there was something *in* that miserable spiritualism, so we could send them word. That Tennessee village would set up a monument to Billings, then, and his autograph would outsell Satan's. Well, they had grand times at that reception— a small-fry noble from Hoboken told me all about it—Sir Richard Duffer, Baronet."

"What, Sandy, a nobleman from Hoboken? How is that?"

"Easy enough. Duffer kept a sausage-shop and never saved a cent in his life because he used to give all his spare meat to the poor, in a quiet way. Not tramps, — no, the other sort—the sort that will starve before they will beg—honest square people out of work. Dick used to watch hungry-looking men and women and children, and track them home, and find out all about them from the neighbors, and then feed them and find them work. As nobody ever

saw him give anything to anybody,
he had the reputation of being mean;
he died with it, too, and everybody
said it was a good riddance; but the
minute he landed here, they made him
a baronet, and the very first words
Dick the sausage-maker of Hoboken
heard when he stepped upon the
heavenly shore were, 'Welcome, Sir
Richard Duffer!' It surprised him
some, because he thought he had
reasons to believe he was pointed for
a warmer climate than this one."

All of a sudden the whole region
fairly rocked under the crash of eleven
hundred and one thunder blasts, all
let off at once, and Sandy says,—

"There, that's for the barkeep."

I jumped up and says,—

Extract from Captain

"Then let's be moving along, Sandy; we don't want to miss any of this thing, you know."

"Keep your seat," he says; "he is only just telegraphed, that is all."

"How?"

"That blast only means that he has been sighted from the signal-station. He is off Sandy Hook. The committees will go down to meet him, now, and escort him in. There will be ceremonies and delays; they won't be coming up the Bay for a considerable time, yet. It is several billion miles away, anyway."

"*I* could have been a barkeeper and a hard lot just as well as not," says I, remembering the lonesome way I arrived, and how there wasn't any committee nor anything.

"I notice some regret in your voice," says Sandy, "and it is natural enough; but let bygones be bygones; you went according to your lights, and it is too late now to mend the thing."

"No, let it slide, Sandy, I don't mind. But you've got a Sandy Hook *here*, too, have you?"

"We've got everything here, just as it is below. All the States and Territories of the Union, and all the kingdoms of the earth and the islands of the sea are laid out here just as they are on the globe—all the same shape they are down there, and all graded to the relative size, only each State and realm and island is a good many billion times bigger here than it is below. There goes another blast."

Extract from Captain

"What is that one for?"

"That is only another fort answering the first one. They each fire eleven hundred and one thunder blasts at a single dash—it is the usual salute for an eleventh-hour guest; a hundred for each hour and an extra one for the guest's sex; if it was a woman we would know it by their leaving off the extra gun."

"How do we know there's eleven hundred and one, Sandy, when they all go off at once?—and yet we certainly do know."

"Our intellects are a good deal sharpened up, here, in some ways, and that is one of them. Numbers and sizes and distances are so great, here, that we have to be made so we can *feel* them—our old ways of counting and measuring and ciphering wouldn't ever give us an idea of them, but would only confuse us and oppress us and make our heads ache."

After some more talk about this, I says: "Sandy, I notice that I hardly ever see a white angel; where I run across one white angel, I strike as many as a hundred million copper-colored ones—people that can't speak English. How is that?"

"Well, you will find it the same in any State or Territory of the American corner of heaven you choose to go to. I have shot along, a whole week on a stretch, and gone millions and millions of miles, through perfect swarms of angels, without ever seeing a single white one, or hearing a word I could understand. You see, Amer-

ica was occupied a billion years and
more, by Injuns and Aztecs, and that
sort of folks, before a white man ever
set his foot in it. During the first
three hundred years after Columbus's discovery, there wasn't ever
more than one good lecture audience
of white people, all put together, in
America—I mean the whole thing,
British Possessions and all; in the beginning of our century there were only
6,000,000 or 7,000,000 — say seven;
12,000,000 or 14,000,000 in 1825; say
23,000,000 in 1850; 40,000,000 in
1875. Our death-rate has always
been 20 in 1000 per annum. Well,
140,000 died the first year of the
century; 280,000 the twenty-fifth
year; 500,000 the fiftieth year; about
a million the seventy-fifth year.

Now I am going to be liberal about this thing, and consider that fifty million whites have died in America from the beginning up to to-day— make it sixty, if you want to; make it a hundred million—it's no difference about a few millions one way or t'other. Well, now, you can see, yourself, that when you come to spread a little dab of people like that over these hundreds of billions of miles of American territory here in heaven, it is like scattering a ten-cent box of homœopathic pills over the Great Sahara and expecting to find them again. You can't expect us to amount to anything in heaven, and we *don't*—now that is the simple fact, and we have got to do the best we can with it. The learned men from other

planets and other systems come here
and hang around a while, when they
are touring around the Kingdom, and
then go back to their own section of
heaven and write a book of travels,
and they give America about five lines
in it. And what do they say about
us? They say this wilderness is popu-
lated with a scattering few hundred
thousand billions of red angels, with
now and then a curiously complected
diseased one. You see, they think
we whites and the occasional nigger
are Injuns that have been bleached
out or blackened by some leprous
disease or other—for some peculiarly
rascally *sin*, mind you. It is a mighty
sour pill for us all, my friend—even
the modestest of us, let alone the other
kind, that think they are going to be

received like a long-lost government
bond, and hug Abraham into the
bargain. I haven't asked you any of
the particulars, Captain, but I judge
it goes without saying—if my experience is worth anything — that
there wasn't much of a hooraw made
over you when you arrived — now
was there?"

"Don't mention it, Sandy," says I,
coloring up a little; " I wouldn't have
had the family see it for any amount
you are a mind to name. Change the
subject, Sandy, change the subject."

"Well, do you think of settling in
the California department of bliss?"

"I don't know. I wasn't calculating on doing anything really definite
in that direction till the family come.
I thought I would just look around,

meantime, in a quiet way, and make up my mind. Besides, I know a good many dead people, and I was calculating to hunt them up and swap a little gossip with them about friends, and old times, and one thing or another, and ask them how they like it here, as far as they have got. I reckon my wife will want to camp in the California range, though, because most all her departed will be there, and she likes to be with folks she knows."

"Don't you let her. You see what the Jersey district of heaven is, for whites; well, the Californian district is a thousand times worse. It swarms with a mean kind of leather-headed mud-colored angels—and your nearest white neighbor is likely to be a million miles away. *What a man*

mostly misses, in heaven, is company
—company of his own sort and color and language. I have come near settling in the European part of heaven once or twice on that account."

"Well, why didn't you, Sandy?"

"Oh, various reasons. For one thing, although you *see* plenty of whites there, you can't understand any of them, hardly, and so you go about as hungry for talk as you do here. I like to look at a Russian or a German or an Italian—I even like to look at a Frenchman if I ever have the luck to catch him engaged in anything that ain't indelicate—but *looking* don't cure the hunger—what you want is talk."

"Well, there's England, Sandy— the English district of heaven."

Extract from Captain

"Yes, but it is not so very much better than this end of the heavenly domain. As long as you run across Englishmen born this side of three hundred years ago, you are all right; but the minute you get back of Elizabeth's time the language begins to fog up, and the further back you go the foggier it gets. I had some talk with one Langland and a man by the name of Chaucer — old-time poets — but it was no use, I couldn't quite understand them, and they couldn't quite understand me. I have had letters from them since, but it is such broken English I can't make it out. Back of those men's time the English are just simply foreigners, nothing more, nothing less; they talk Danish, German, Norman French, and sometimes a mixture of all three; back of *them*, they talk Latin, and ancient British, Irish, and Gaelic; and then back of these come billions and billions of pure savages that talk a gibberish that Satan himself couldn't understand. The fact is, where you strike one man in the English settlements that you can understand, you wade through awful swarms that talk something you can't make head nor tail of. You see, every country on earth has been overlaid so often, in the course of a billion years, with different kinds of people and different sorts of languages, that this sort of mongrel business was bound to be the result in heaven."

"Sandy," says I, "did you see a good many of the great people history tells about?"

"Yes—plenty. I saw kings and all sorts of distinguished people."

"Do the kings rank just as they did below?"

"No; a body can't bring his rank up here with him. Divine right is a good-enough earthly romance, but it don't go, here. Kings drop down to the general level as soon as they reach the realms of grace. I knew Charles the Second very well—one of the most popular comedians in the English section—draws first rate. There are better, of course—people that were never heard of on earth—but Charles is making a very good reputation indeed, and is considered a rising man. Richard the Lion-hearted is in the prize-ring, and coming into considerable favor. Henry the Eighth is a

tragedian, and the scenes where he
kills people are done to the very life.
Henry the Sixth keeps a religious-
book stand."

"Did you ever see Napoleon,
Sandy?"

"Often—sometimes in the Corsican
range, sometimes in the French.   He
always hunts up a conspicuous place,
and goes frowning around with his
arms folded and his field-glass under
his arm, looking as grand, gloomy and
peculiar as his reputation calls for,
and very much bothered because he
don't stand as high, here, for a soldier,
as he expected to."

"Why, who stands higher?"

"Oh, a *lot* of people *we* never heard
of before—the shoemaker and horse-
doctor and knife - grinder kind, you

know — clodhoppers from goodness knows where that never handled a sword or fired a shot in their lives —but the soldiership was in them, though they never had a chance to show it. But here they take their right place, and Cæsar and Napoleon and Alexander have to take a back seat. The greatest military genius our world ever produced was a bricklayer from somewhere back of Boston —died during the Revolution—by the name of Absalom Jones. Wherever he goes, crowds flock to see him. You see, everybody knows that if he had had a chance he would have shown the world some generalship that would have made all generalship before look like child's play and 'prentice work. But he never got a chance;

he tried heaps of times to enlist as a
private, but he had lost both thumbs
and a couple of front teeth, and the
recruiting sergeant wouldn't pass him.
However, as I say, everybody knows,
now, what he *would* have been, and
so they flock by the million to get a
glimpse of him whenever they hear he
is going to be anywhere. Cæsar, and
Hannibal, and Alexander, and Napoleon are all on his staff, and ever so
many more great generals; but the
public hardly care to look at *them*
when *he* is around. Boom! There
goes another salute. The barkeeper's
off quarantine now."

Sandy and I put on our things.
Then we made a wish, and in a second
we were at the reception-place. We

stood on the edge of the ocean of space, and looked out over the dimness, but couldn't make out anything. Close by us was the Grand Stand—tier on tier of dim thrones rising up toward the zenith. From each side of it spread away the tiers of seats for the general public. They spread away for leagues and leagues—you couldn't see the ends. They were empty and still, and hadn't a cheerful look, but looked dreary, like a theatre before anybody comes—gas turned down. Sandy says,—

"We'll sit down here and wait. We'll see the head of the procession come in sight away off yonder pretty soon, now."

Says I,—

"It's pretty lonesome, Sandy; I

reckon there's a hitch somewheres. Nobody but just you and me—it ain't much of a display for the barkeeper."

"Don't you fret, it's all right. There'll be one more gun-fire—then you'll see."

In a little while we noticed a sort of a lightish flush, away off on the horizon.

"Head of the torchlight procession," says Sandy.

It spread, and got lighter and brighter; soon it had a strong glare like a locomotive headlight; it kept on getting brighter and brighter till it was like the sun peeping above the horizon-line at sea—the big red rays shot high up into the sky.

"Keep your eyes on the Grand Stand and the miles of seats—sharp!"

says Sandy, "and listen for the gun-fire."

Just then it burst out, "Boom-boom-boom!" like a million thunder-storms in one, and made the whole heavens rock. Then there was a sudden and awful glare of light all about us, and in that very instant every one of the millions of seats was occupied, and as far as you could see, in both directions, was just a solid pack of people, and the place was all splendidly lit up! It was enough to take a body's breath away. Sandy says,—

"That is the way we do it here. No time fooled away; nobody strag-gling in after the curtain's up. Wish-ing is quicker work than travelling. A quarter of a second ago these folks

were millions of miles from here.
When they heard the last signal, all
they had to do was to wish, and here
they are."

The prodigious choir struck up,—

> We long to hear thy voice,
> To see thee face to face.

It was noble music, but the unedu-
cated chipped in and spoilt it, just as
the congregations used to do on earth.

The head of the procession began
to pass, now, and it was a wonderful
sight. It swept along, thick and solid,
five hundred thousand angels abreast,
and every angel carrying a torch and
singing—the whirring thunder of the
wings made a body's head ache. You
could follow the line of the procession
back, and slanting upward into the

117

sky, far away in a glittering snaky rope, till it was only a faint streak in the distance. The rush went on and on, for a long time, and at last, sure enough, along comes the barkeeper, and then everybody rose, and a cheer went up that made the heavens shake, I tell you! He was all smiles, and had his halo tilted over one ear in a cocky way, and was the most satisfied-looking saint I ever saw. While he marched up the steps of the Grand Stand, the choir struck up,—

> The whole wide heaven groans,
> And waits to hear that voice."

There were four gorgeous tents standing side by side in the place of honor, on a broad railed platform in the centre of the Grand Stand, with a shining guard of honor round about them. The tents had been shut up all this time. As the barkeeper climbed along up, bowing and smiling to everybody, and at last got to the platform, these tents were jerked up aloft all of a sudden, and we saw four noble thrones of gold, all caked with jewels, and in the two middle ones sat old white-whiskered men, and in the two others a couple of the most glorious and gaudy giants, with platter halos and beautiful armor. All the millions went down on their knees, and stared, and looked glad, and burst out into a joyful kind of murmurs. They said,—

"Two archangels!—that is splendid. Who can the others be?"

The archangels gave the barkeeper

a stiff little military bow; the two old
men rose; one of them said, "Moses
and Esau welcome thee!" and then
all the four vanished, and the thrones
were empty.

The barkeeper looked a little disappointed, for he was calculating to
hug those old people, I judge; but it
was the gladdest and proudest mul-
titude you ever saw—because they
had seen Moses and Esau. Everybody was saying, "Did you see them?
—I did—Esau's side face was to me,
but I saw Moses full in the face, just
as plain as I see you this minute!"

The procession took up the barkeeper and moved on with him again,
and the crowd broke up and scattered.
As we went along home, Sandy said it
was a great success, and the barkeeper

would have a right to be proud of it
forever. And he said *we* were in luck,
too; said we might attend receptions
for forty thousand years to come, and
not have a chance to see a brace of
such grand moguls as Moses and
Esau. We found afterwards that we
had come near seeing another patriarch, and likewise a genuine prophet
besides, but at the last moment they
sent regrets. Sandy said there would
be a monument put up there, where
Moses and Esau had stood, with the
date and circumstances, and all about
the whole business, and travellers
would come for thousands of years
and gawk at it, and climb over it,
and scribble their names on it.

THE END.